WALT DISNEY'S

UNCLE $CROOGE

in

The Phantom of Notre Duck

WALT DISNEY PUBLICATIONS, INC.
BURBANK, CALIFORNIA

Michael Lynton—Vice President, Marketing, Publications   Randy Achee—Publisher
Len Wein—Editor-in-Chief   Bob Foster—Editor   Sally Prendergast—Marketing Manager
Andrea Beam—National Sales Manager   Barbara Pietuch—Production Manager

THE MANY FACES OF UNCLE SCROOGE

Ask any fan to describe Uncle Scrooge, and chances are good he will tell you about the adventure stories of the 1950s. Those are the comics that shaped Scrooge's character and made him a star. From the first feature-length adventure, Carl Barks realized that he was forming a hero and shifted focus from McDuck the miser of the 1940s to McDuck the entrepreneur. Scrooge remained a businessman, but one who had **earned** his dollars by pulling them from the earth with his bare hands. That established, the money could be relied on to buy tickets or technology for shuttling the ducks to Atlantis, the Himalayas, even the asteroid belt: the process of finding more treasure was limited only by Barks' imagination. In many ways, exotic adventure itself became the hero of the Scrooge comics. McDuck was the gimmick that got each story rolling, but the quest helped to focus his moneylust and lend direction to the plot.

All that changed in the 1960s, a decade when foreign lands lost much of their glamour and even the ocean floor seemed devoid of romance, disgorging industrial waste rather than sunken treasure. To give his comics new focus, Barks created a series of villains as foils for McDuck: the sorceress Magica de Spell, the pigface Porkman de Lardo, and the Phantom of Notre Duck, a shadowy doppelgänger for Scrooge who could have been one of Barks' strongest creations. But without the treasure quest to invoke romantic ideals and provide a definite goal, the stories devolved into comedic free-for-alls, with Scrooge and the villain scrambling for possession of a coveted dime, ruby, or flute.

Nowhere is this more obvious than in "The Phantom of Notre Duck," a tale with plenty of spooky potential but no constructive goal: Scrooge spends the entire story chasing around the cathedral simply to recover a stolen flute. Nor is there a true motive for villainy; in the end Barks defused all conflicts by revealing that Scrooge would have been happy to lend the thief any amount of money. Even the Phantom's physical resemblance to McDuck, which might have added a threatening undercurrent to the plot, turns into a toss-off gag. "All I can say," quips Donald, "is such a face must go with guys who like to play with money!" What finally saves the story is its emphasis on play. With games of hide-and-seek around the cathedral, characters escaping as fast as they get locked up, and everyone emerging happy, "The Phantom of Notre Duck" makes up in buoyancy what it lacks in romantic vision.

Barks wrote only ten more Scrooge comics before retiring in 1966, yet McDuck remained central to his life and art. Three years later, when editor Chase Craig pressured him into scripting stories for a new line of **Junior Woodchuck** comics, Barks took the opportunity to return to Scrooge's roots and rethink the character. "I used Uncle Scrooge as the villain," he confided in a letter to Michael Barrier. "Analysing all the things you fans have written and said, I've concluded that you all liked him best when he was the menace in the duck stories. When he became the hero, with his own book, I had to be careful how bad I made him. Anyway, in the current story he is fighting dirty against the Junior Woodchucks who are trying to save a whale that got washed ashore by a tidal wave. Uncle S. wants to render the frantic mammal into countless barrels of whale oil. In the previous story Uncle S. was going to cut down the Black Forest of Duckburg and turn the whole ecology into a suburbia."

So the Woodchucks stories became fresh vehicles for Scrooge. If their moral framework of good scouts versus bad industrialist seems forced at times, it is also refreshing simply to have a framework after the giddiness of the 1960s. Refreshing, too, to notice how well the old miser survives the passage of years. Had Barks continued to write in the 1980s, we might have seen yet another face of Scrooge McDuck.

—Giles Moran

Creator Credits

Front cover by Larry Mayer, based on a layout by Carl Barks.

"The Phantom of Notre Duck," written and drawn by Carl Barks (first published in US 60, 1965).

"Whale of a Good Deed," written by Carl Barks, art by Kay Wright (first published in Huey, Dewey and Louie Junior Woodchucks 7, 1970).

"Somethin' Fishy Here," written and drawn by Carl Barks (first published in US one-shot 456, 1953).

ISBN 1-56115-022-3

1 3 5 7 9 8 6 4 2

THAT EXPLAINS IT! THE THIEF STOLE THE FIFE BECAUSE HE HEARD ME SAY IT'D OPEN MY MONEY VAULT! I'VE *GOT TO* GET THAT FIFE BACK!

OW!

HE SNAPPED MY FINGERS IN AN OLD *PURSE* THAT SOMEBODY THREW IN HERE SOMETIME!

GUARD, HOW CAN I GET TO THE *BASEMENT* — OR WHATEVER'S ON THE OTHER SIDE OF THAT FOUNTAIN WALL?

THE CATHEDRAL *HAS NO* BASEMENT, SIR! THE THIEF YOU'VE DISCOVERED MUST HAVE *TUNNELED* TO THE FOUNTAIN FROM THE CATACOMBS!

THEN SHOW ME TO THE CATACOMBS! I'VE *GOT TO* GET THAT FIFE BACK! IT'S THE *ONLY* FIFE THAT CAN OPEN MY MONEY VAULT!

BESIDES, IT COST ME *EIGHTY CENTS*!

TUNNELS AND CATACOMBS! I BET THAT THIEF IS THE FAMOUS *PHANTOM* OF NOTRE DUCK!

WITH SECRET PASSAGES ALL OVER THIS SPOOKY PLACE!

MY BONNIE LIES OVER THE OCEAN

WAK!

OH, OH!

MAKE A PILE OF **CUSHIONS** UNDER UNCA SCROOGE, QUICK!

IF THAT ROPE BREAKS, WE'LL BE SUDDENLY OUT OF RICH RELATIVES!

(G-GULP!) THE PHANTOM'S **HUNG** ME LIKE A DRIP-DRY SHIRT!

THAT GUY PLAYS **ROUGH!**

I'LL GET UP ON THE **ROOF** AND SEE IF I CAN LOWER YOU DOWN, UNCLE SCROOGE!

MY KEEN MIND TELLS ME TO BE **CAREFUL!** THE PHANTOM MAY BE PLANNING TO HANG **ME** UP TO DRY, TOO!

IN FACT HE PROBABLY WANTS TO TRAP **ALL OF US** LONG ENOUGH TO STAGE A RAID ON UNCLE SCROOGE'S MONEY BIN!

WHOA! WHAT NOW?.... THAT MUST BE HIM **THERE** — HEADING FOR A SHORT CUT TO THE STREET!

HE DOESN'T KNOW I'M HERE! I CAN **GRAB HIM** AND SAVE UNCLE SCROOGE'S FIFE AT THE SAME TIME!

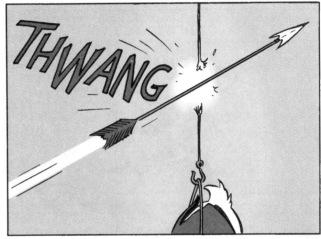

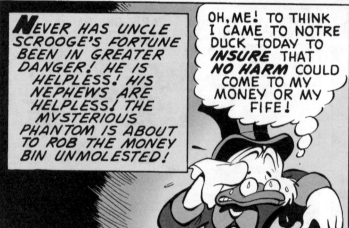

I—I'D HAVE FREED YOU AS SOON AS I FINISHED MY **WORK** HERE!

I'LL BET! WHAT **IS** YOUR WORK HERE — THIS COIN CATHEDRAL?

YES (SOB)! AND NOW I'LL NEVER KNOW HOW MY **MASTERPIECE** WILL LOOK COMPLETED!

OH, I WOULDN'T SAY THAT! I KINDA WANT TO SEE HOW IT WOULD LOOK, **MYSELF**!

YOU FOUND YOU COULDN'T RAKE ENOUGH COINS OUT OF THE WISHING FOUNTAIN IN ONE LIFETIME TO BUILD THIS REPLICA OF NOTRE DUCK, EH?

Y-YES, TO MY SORROW!

SO WHEN I HEARD YOU SAY THIS **FIFE** WOULD OPEN YOUR VAST MONEY BIN I WENT **MAD** WITH **GREED**!

AND WHAT A WASTE OF ENERGY, PHANTOM! IF YOU'D TOLD ME YOU HAD **FUN** LIKE THIS GOING WITH **MONEY**, I'D HAVE **LOANED** YOU ALL THE COINS YOU NEEDED!

PROVIDED, OF COURSE, THAT **I COULD HELP** WITH THE BUILDING!

FOR PETE'S SAKE, UNCLE SCROOGE! ARE YOU SO GOONY OVER THIS MONEY PLAYHOUSE THAT YOU'RE *FORGIVING* THIS HOODED HOOD?

HE'S THE TERRIBLE *PHANTOM!* AREN'T YOU AT LEAST GOING TO MAKE HIM *SHOW HIS UGLY FACE?*

YES!... PHANTOM, SHOW US YOUR UGLY FACE!

UNCLE SCROOGE!... HE LOOKS LIKE *UNCLE SCROOGE!*

ALL I CAN SAY IS SUCH A FACE MUST GO WITH GUYS WHO LIKE TO PLAY WITH *MONEY!*

So UNCLE SCROOGE *GETS HIS FIFE BACK,* AND NOTRE DUCK *GETS TO KEEP ITS PHANTOM!*

HEY! HOW COME YOU'RE NOT OPENING YOUR VAULT DOOR WITH A TOOTLING *TUNE,* UNCLE SCROOGE?

I CHANGED MY MIND ABOUT THE FIFE LOCK, DONALD, AND WENT BACK TO THE OLD COMBINATION OF *NUMBERS!*

CLICK

AFTER BEING PART OF THAT PIPE ORGAN I SORT OF LOST MY EAR FOR *MUSIC!*

So- WELL, LUCKY ME! A **FREE** NEWSPAPER!

"COINS AND BANKNOTES NOW **WORTHLESS**!.... CONGRESS MAKES FISH THE NEW **MONEY** OF THE LAND!"

OH, MY **WASTED** DAYS! I'M PENNILESS! MY THREE CUBIC ACRES OF CASH ARE WORTH **NOTHING**!

I HAVEN'T EVEN ONE LITTLE **MINNOW** TO BUY A CRUST OF BREAD!

HAR! HAR! HAR! HE'S TAKING IT LIKE A TROUT TAKES A FLY! THIS IS THE FUNNIEST GAG I EVER PULLED IN MY LIFE!

YOU BETTER KEEP YOUR FINGERS CROSSED AND HOPE IT **STAYS** FUNNY!

WELL, THERE'S NO USE CRYING OVER BAD LUCK! I'LL GET A **JOB** AND START LIFE ALL OVER AGAIN!

I'LL HELP YOU PAINT YOUR BOAT FOR A SACKFUL OF THOSE **FISH**!

WHY.... OKAY!

WHALE OF A GOOD DEED

Walt Disney
HUEY, DEWEY and LOUIE
THE JUNIOR WOODCHUCKS

DUCKBURG WILL ALWAYS REMEMBER TIDAL WAVE PLUVIUS!

THE GIANT WAVE HAS WASHED THE SUBMARINE GARDENS ONTO THE ROOF OF THE ASTRODOME!

AND PUT TWO TUGBOATS IN EVERY GARAGE!

LUCKILY THERE WAS PLENTY OF WARNING!

NOBODY IS GETTING HIS TAIL FEATHERS WET!

THE JUNIOR WOODCHUCKS WILL NEVER FORGET THE TIDAL WAVE EITHER!

TODAY WILL BE A DAY OF *GOOD DEEDS*, TROOPERS!

YES, GREAT T.O.P. B.R.A.S.S.! *

*THUNDERBOLT OF OMNISCIENT PERSPICACITY AND BOSS RAMROD OF ABOUNDING SUCCOR SPREADERS!

TROOP-A, UNDER GENERALS HUEY, LOUIE AND DEWEY DUCK, WILL SUCCOR THE DISTRESSED ALONG DISMAL SHORES!

YES, GREAT T.O.P. B.R.A.S.S.!

THAT OLD CHEST LOOKS DISTRESSED!

NIXIE, NIXIE, TROOPERS! YOU'RE TO AID ONLY THINGS THAT GROAN, CRY OR GASP!

IF YOU GIRLS WILL GROAN, CRY OR GASP, WE'LL HELP YOU SHOVEL THAT MUD!

GET LOST, WOODCHUCKS!

WE ARE MEMBERS OF THE *LITTLEST CHICKADEES!*

AND WE'RE DOING OUR OWN THING AT AIDING THE DISTRESSED!

WELL, THANK THEIR HIGHNESSES FOR LITTLE FAVORS!

WE DIDN'T WANT TO SHOVEL MUD ANYWAY!

LOOK! A WOODCHUCK *TROUBLE* FLAG ON THAT DISTANT DUNE!

WOOSH!

BRING MORE *KETTLES*, MEN!

AND FETCH THE *STEAM WINCH* FROM MY WHALING DOCK!

YES, MR. McDUCK!

JUST FOR SOILING MY SILK HAT I'M GOING TO MAKE OIL OUT OF *ALL FOUR QUARTERS* OF THAT SASSY WHALE!

OH, WOEFUL DAY!

UNCA SCROOGE IS GOING TO DRAG *ALL* OF MUDDY DICK ONTO HIS LAND!

HE MUSTN'T! MAYBE *ENOUGH* OF US CAN OUTPULL HIM!

FIND *ROPES!* FIND *ANCHORS!*

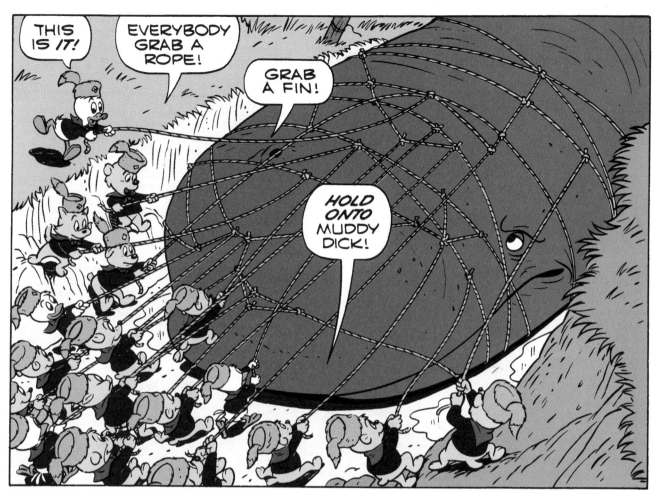